Garfield

Admit it, Odie's O.K.!

JIM DAVIS

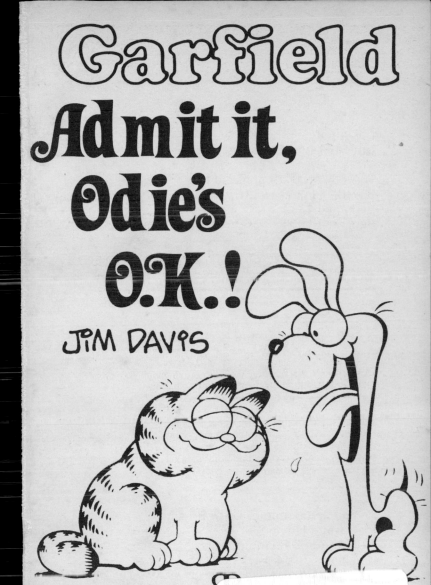

Ravett

Copyright © 1983
United Feature Syndicate, Inc.

This edition first published by
Ravette Limited 1983
Reprinted 1984
Reprinted 1985

Printed and bound in Great Britain
for Ravette Limited,
12 Star Road, Partridge Green,
Horsham, Sussex RH13 8RA
by Cox & Wyman Ltd,
Reading

ISBN 0 906710 09 X

© 1982 United Feature Syndicate, Inc.

© 1982 United Feature Syndicate, Inc.

© 1982 United Feature Syndicate, Inc.

JIM DAVIS   1-11

GARFIELD! WHAT HAPPENED!

QUICK! GET THE LICENSE NUMBER OF THAT DOG!

© 1982 United Feature Syndicate, Inc.

© 1982 United Feature Syndicate, Inc.

© 1982 United Feature Syndicate, Inc.

BARK

ARRRGH!

VERY FUNNY, ODIE. NOW GET YOUR FACE OFF THE WINDOW

GETTING OUT OF THIS TREE WILL BE SIMPLER THAN I THOUGHT

CHUG!

YOU'RE A REAL BEAR UNTIL YOU'VE HAD YOUR FIRST CUP OF COFFEE, AREN'T YOU?

AND THEN I'M THE SWEETEST SO-AND-SO AROUND

© 1982 United Feature Syndicate, Inc.

© 1982 United Feature Syndicate, Inc.

© 1982 United Feature Syndicate, Inc.

JIM DAVIS 4-2

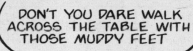

DON'T YOU DARE WALK ACROSS THE TABLE WITH THOSE MUDDY FEET

© 1982 United Feature Syndicate, Inc.

9-2

WHAM!

BIFF!

BAM!

JiM DAViS   9-24

© 1982 United Feature Syndicate, Inc.

© 1982 United Feature Syndicate, Inc.

WAH-CHOO!

WAH-
CHOO!

© 1982 United Feature Syndicate, Inc.

6-28

DON'T LOOK IN HERE, JON. IT'S NOT A PRETTY SIGHT

JIM DAVIS   11-5

JIM DAVIS

© 1981 United Feature Syndicate, Inc.

6-14

© 1982 United Feature Syndicate, Inc.

© 1982 United Feature Syndicate, Inc.

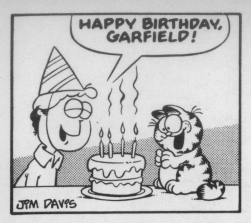

© 1982 United Feature Syndicate, Inc.

© 1982 United Feature Syndicate, Inc.

HELLO. I'M NERMAL, THE WORLD'S CUTEST KITTEN, HERE TO DO CUTE KITTEN THINGS IN ORDER TO CHARM THE PANTS OFF YOUR OWNER AND POINT OUT HOW UNCUTE YOU ARE

© 1982 United Feature Syndicate, Inc.

© 1982 United Feature Syndicate, Inc.

© 1982 United Feature Syndicate, Inc.